The Learning Works

Create a City

A Complete Framework for Students to Use in Creating an Original City

Grades 5–8

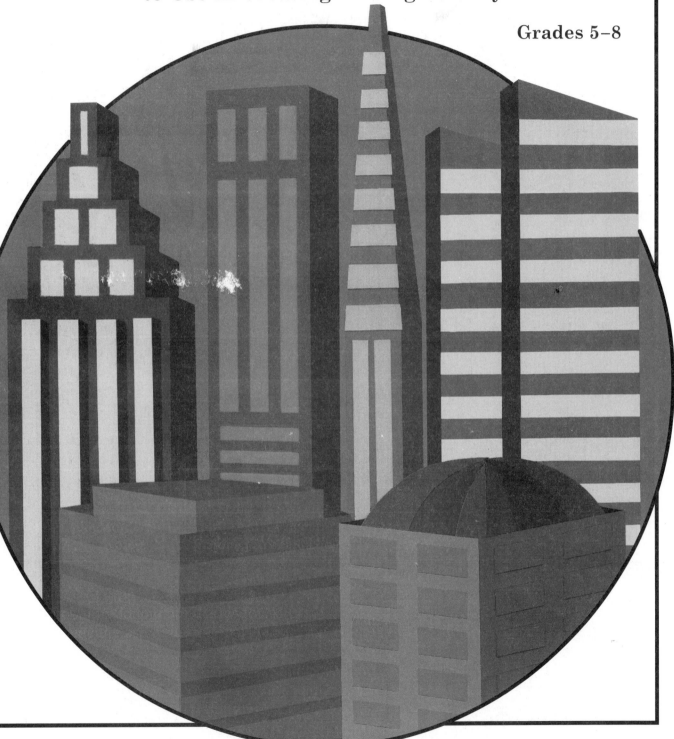

Written by Charlotte Jaffe & Barbara Doherty
Illustrated by Bev Armstrong • Cover Art by Lucyna A.M. Green

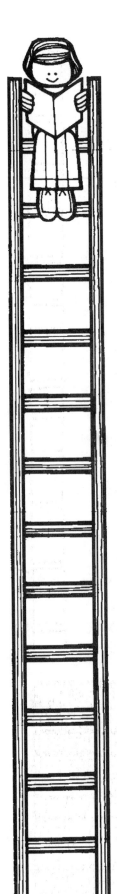

The Learning Works

Illustration:
  Bev Armstrong

Editing and Text Design:
  Clark Editorial & Design

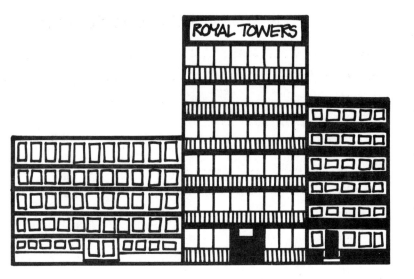

Copyright © 1999
The Learning Works, Inc.

Creative Teaching Press, Inc.
Huntington Beach, CA 92649

Printed in the United States of America.

Table of Contents

Introduction 5–6

SECTION I • Making Decisions

Naming Your City 8
Location 9
History 10–11
Physical Features 12–13
Cultures and Diversity 14–15
Demographics 16–17
Group Worksheets I, II, and III 18–20

SECTION II • Creating Your City

Government 22–23
Business and Industry 24–25
Education 26–27
Architecture 28–29
Shopping and Dining 30–31
Transportation 32–33
Landmarks 34–35
Climate 36–37
Cultural Life 38–39
Recreation 40–41
Creating a Budget 42–43
City Council Debates 44–45
City Statistics 46
Reporting About Your City 47–48

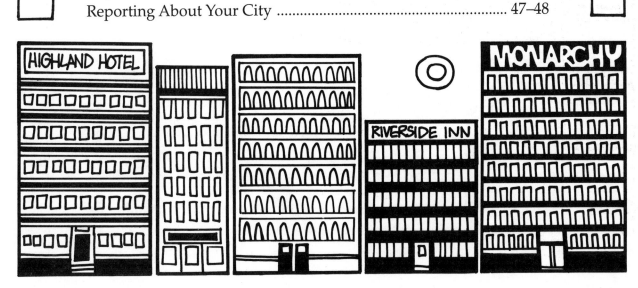

Table of Contents
(continued)

SECTION III • Project Ideas

It's Travel Time 50

Create a Travel Poster 51

Regional Food Fest 52–53

City Symbols 54

Map Your City 55

Musical Tribute 56

Create a Professional Sports Team 57

City Mural 58

City Poetry 59

The Big Story 60

Annual Events 61

Wish You Were Here 62

Create a Character 63–67

Meet the Character 68

In Honor Of 69

City Scrapbook 70–71

City Tour 72

A Sense-ational City 73

Musical Performance 74

City Shirts 75

Refreshment Stand 76

SECTION IV • City Celebrations Day

City Celebrations Day Planning Sheets I and II 78–79

Display Plan 80

Invitation Form 81

Thank-You Letter 82

Certificate of Participation 83

Evaluation Form 84

Section V • Reference Materials

City Tourist Bureaus 86–87

Bibliography and City Internet Sites 88

Introduction

Create a City presents a variety of exciting and challenging activities that will engage students in the process of developing an imaginary city. The main objective is to increase the students' knowledge of the elements that many cities share, as well as the elements that make cities unique. By designing a fictitious city, deciding its history, and developing its government, industry, architecture, and other city features, students will gain insight into how cities originate, grow, and change.

This unit is designed for cooperative learning groups of three to five students. The activities can be done during class time or completed as homework assignments. The *Create a City* unit can be completed in four to six weeks depending on the amount of time allotted for each section.

Create a City is divided into five sections:

- Making Decisions
- Creating Your City
- Project Ideas
- City Celebrations Day
- Reference Materials

Section I • Making Decisions
In this section, students work in groups to gather facts and brainstorm possible answers to stimulating activity questions. Reference materials are needed to accomplish the tasks on many of the activity pages. Once they have completed the Making Decisions section of the book, students are ready to move on to the next phase of the project.

Section II • Creating Your City
These activities help the students begin the development of their imaginary cities by applying the concepts of a real city to their fictitious ones. By completing the activities in this section, students will practice the following skills: creative thinking, evaluating, analyzing, synthesizing, and drawing conclusions. The section ends with directions for reporting on the new city by completing a "City Council Study."

Introduction
(continued)

Section III • Project Ideas

This section provides the opportunity for students to demonstrate the results of their work on their cities through models, presentations, musical tributes, and poetry. These activities can be managed in three different ways:

1. Have each group do all of the projects provided. This will require each student to take responsibility for more than one assignment.

2. Decide how many projects each student should complete, and then select the specific projects that each group should do. You can assign the same project to all student groups, or give different projects to each group.

3. Give all the project sheets to each group and let the students decide which ones they will do. You may choose to require that all groups complete a special project and then allow group members to select additional projects.

Encourage each group to use a variety of project ideas so that the display on City Celebrations Day will be more diverse and interesting.

Section IV • City Celebrations Day

The activities in this part of the book include directions for presenting the work of each group to classmates, other students, parents, teachers, administrators, and community members. Students plan their presentations, organize their displays, and write invitations.

Section V • Reference Materials

This section includes Tourist Bureau listings, a bibliography, and a list of city Web sites. Students can use these reference materials to obtain information about existing cities to help them make their creative projects more successful.

Note: If students need additional space to record their responses, ask them to use the blank sides of their worksheets and activity pages.

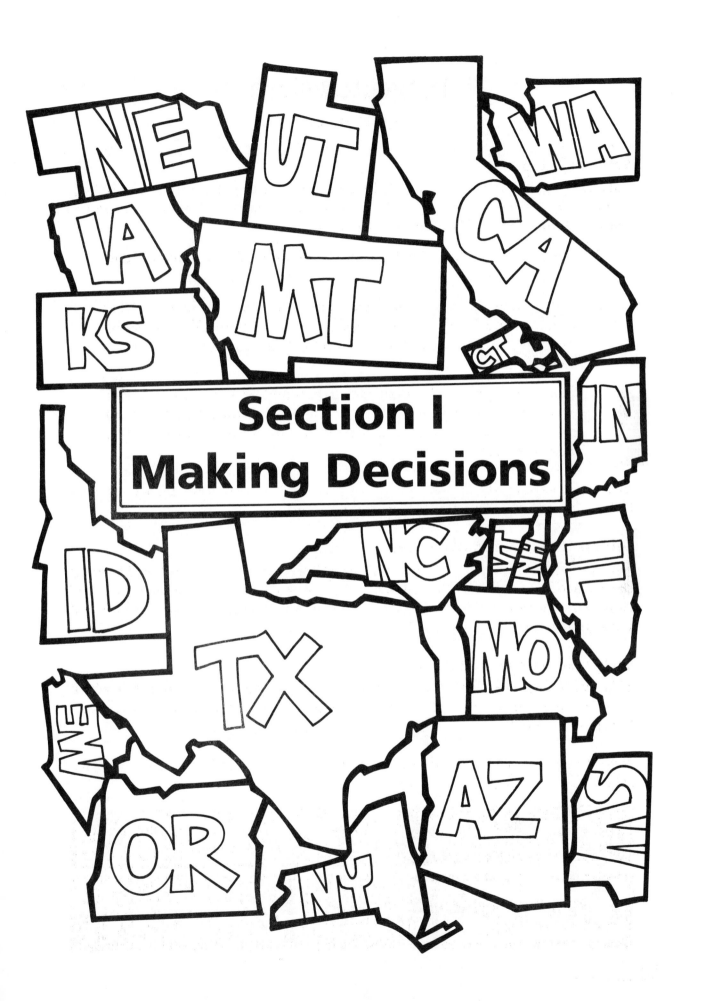

Section I
Making Decisions

Name _____

Naming Your City

Have you ever wondered how the city or town where you live got its name? Some names are derived from physical features in the area. The city of Hot Springs, Arkansas, takes its name from the mineral-rich springs that flow down the slope of Hot Springs Mountain. Some cities get their names from Native-American words. The name Chicago is borrowed from the Indian word for the Chicago River, *Checagou*. Other cities are named for early settlers in the region. In colonial times, residents in one Virginia settlement heard the news about England from Captain Christopher Newport. Their city became Newport News. Other cities have origins that are more unusual. For example, Truth or Consequences, New Mexico, was named after a popular radio program. Treasure Island, Florida, got its name from early settlers who believed that pirates had buried treasure there.

List some possible names for your city on the lines below. Briefly explain the significance of each name.

1. _____

2. _____

3. _____

4. _____

5. _____

As a group, evaluate each name that was listed. After a thorough discussion, come to an agreement and select a city name. Write your choice here.

_____

You may decide to give your city a nickname. Many cities have them—Orlando, Florida, is called "The City Beautiful." Philadelphia, Pennsylvania, is known as "The City of Brotherly Love." Write your ideas on the lines below. Evaluate them with your group, and choose the one you all like the best.

_____   _____

_____   _____

Name _____

Location

When describing a city's location, it is helpful to give as much information as possible. The following is an example you may want to use as a guide in describing the location of your new city.

Philadelphia is located on the southeastern side of the state of Pennsylvania. Philadelphia is a port city located on the Delaware River. It is about 40 miles from the Delaware Bay and about 50 miles from the Atlantic Ocean. You will find Philadelphia in the approximate center of the metropolitan area that stretches from Boston, Massachusetts, to Washington, D.C.

The system of latitude and longitude is like an address locator for places all over the world. Lines of latitude circle the earth horizontally and measure distances north and south of the equator. The closer one is to 0 degrees latitude, the closer one is to the equator. Lines of longitude circle the earth in a north to south manner and measure distance east or west of the Prime Meridian (in Greenwich, England). When using latitude and longitude, the location of any point on the globe can be indicated in degrees. For example, Philadelphia, Pennsylvania, is located at 40 degrees North latitude and 75 degrees West longitude. San Francisco, California, is located at 37 degrees North latitude and 122 degrees West longitude.

Discuss with your group the basic information concerning the location of your city.

Use the following outline to help you write a description of your city's location.

1. Decide the latitude and longitude of your city. _____

2. Name the state where your city is located. _____

3. Name the surrounding states. _____

Write your description here.

_____

_____

_____

_____

_____

_____

Create a City
© The Learning Works, Inc.

Name _____

History

Many American cities have histories that are unique and interesting. Denver, Colorado, originally was a supply center for mining settlements. The location was an important part of the "Pike's Peak or Bust" gold rush of 1859. Pittsburgh, Pennsylvania, started as Fort Pitt, a British military post named for William Pitt, who was a prime minister of England. Chicago, Illinois, survived the Great Fire of 1871 and was rebuilt into the great city it is today. In 1906, San Francisco, California, was hit with a destructive earthquake that ruined most of the city. It recovered and has become a popular tourist city. During the Civil War, Atlanta, Georgia, was captured by General William T. Sherman. Most of the city's buildings were destroyed at that time. Today it is one of the fastest-growing cities in the United States.

1. With your group, investigate the history of your local city or town.

2. Assign members of your group to research some of the important historical events that took place in the following cities. Have members share their findings with the entire group.

- Charleston, South Carolina
- San Antonio, Texas
- St. Louis, Missouri

- Boston, Massachusetts
- New Orleans, Louisiana
- Baltimore, Maryland

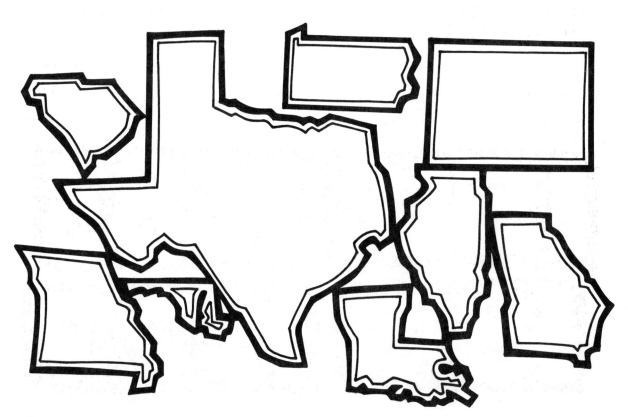

Name _____

History
(continued)

With your group, brainstorm specific details concerning the history of the city you are creating. Record your answers to the following questions.

In what year was your city founded? _____

Tell about the origin of the first settlement. Who were the first people to live in the region?

_____
_____
_____

Relate information about the later settlers of your city. Explain the reasons why they moved to this city.

_____
_____
_____

Discuss a historical event that made an important impact on the citizens of the city. Tell about its significance.

_____
_____
_____

Create a City
© The Learning Works, Inc.

Name _____

Physical Features

The earth's surface is composed of various physical features. These features may take many forms: hills, mountains, craters, cliffs, rivers, lakes, valleys, canyons, and plateaus, to name a few.

Physical features often determine how and where buildings, roads, railroads, airports, and bridges are constructed. In addition, physical features can influence a city's air quality and weather as well as the types of industry conducted there. For example, Juneau, the capital of Alaska, is situated in such a way that it is surrounded on three sides by mountains and by water on the fourth. The roads around Juneau do not extend very far in any direction. It is too expensive to build the roads through the mountains. To reach other areas, the people of Juneau use public and private boats and airplanes.

Briefly describe some of the outstanding physical features of the city in which you live. How have people adapted to these physical features?

_____

_____

_____

_____

_____

Briefly describe an example of how a physical feature may have a negative effect on a city.

_____

_____

_____

_____

_____

Name _____

Physical Features
(continued)

With the other members of your group, discuss the physical features of your new city. Decide which features would be consistent with the location you have given your city. From the list below, select any three physical features for your new city:

- lake
- river
- ocean

- hill(s)
- mountain
- canyon

- island
- cliff
- desert

For each physical feature chosen, complete the following details: type of feature, its name, where it is located, and how it affects your city.

Physical feature #1 is _____

It is called _____

It is located _____

_____

It affects our city _____

_____

Physical feature #2 is _____

It is called _____

It is located _____

_____

It affects our city _____

_____

Physical feature #3 is _____

It is called _____

It is located _____

_____

It affects our city _____

_____

Name _____

Cultures and Diversity

Cities are made up of people from many diverse cultures. Each culture reflects the unique heritage of its people—their language, holidays, customs, foods, clothing, etc. These parts of a culture are often reflected in traditional celebrations. The celebrations may be religious or historical in nature, or may be personal events such as weddings, births, and deaths.

With your group, brainstorm a list of the different cultures that exist where you live.

_____

_____

_____

_____

From the cultures you listed above, list any traditional celebrations that are held in your city.

_____

_____

_____

_____

Does your family observe a special ethnic holiday? If so, describe it here.

_____

_____

_____

_____

_____

_____

_____

_____

Name _____

Cultures and Diversity
(continued)

What cultures help to make up the new city you are creating?

_____

_____

_____

_____

Describe the major contributions each culture has made to your city.

_____

_____

_____

_____

_____

_____

What special holidays are celebrated by the different cultures within your new city?
Describe these events in detail.

_____

_____

_____

_____

_____

_____

Name _____

Demographics

Demographics is the study of a population and its parts. Demographics also involves the study of population and growth. Analyzing demographics helps business owners determine what products are needed, and allows government agencies to anticipate and plan for needed services.

The United States Census Bureau conducts a survey every 10 years to learn about the population of America. The survey includes questions about age, gender, employment, income groups, etc.

Local municipalities sometimes hire demographic specialists to analyze the existing population, land use, water consumption, and the predicted population increase or decrease. This type of study is helpful to the local governing body which may be responsible for large projects that need long-range planning. The demographic information is an important factor to consider in planning for schools, water and waste treatment plants, streets, and other public facilities.

Complete the chart below by researching the cities listed. You may use almanacs, reference books, or the Internet. (A list of Web sites appears in the Bibliography on page 88.)

City	Total Population	Percentage of People Under 30 Years of Age	Rate of Unemployment
Phoenix, AZ			
New York, NY			
Denver, CO			
Chicago, IL			
Miami, FL			

Name _____

Demographics
(continued)

Discuss within your group the demographic statistics of your new city. Record your decisions about the demographics in the spaces below.

City area in square miles _____

Total population _____ Males (%) _____ Females (%) _____

Number of people per square mile _____

Unemployment rate _____

Percentage of people under 16 years of age _____

Average number of children per household _____

Percentage of people living in downtown and suburban areas _____

Percentage of people living in rural areas _____

Percentage of people who use public transportation
to commute to and from work _____

Percentage of households where the highest level
of education is high school _____

Percentage of households where the highest level
of education is college _____

Percentage of people who are registered to vote _____

Percentage of people who regularly perform volunteer work _____

With the members of your group, brainstorm a list of other demographic categories which best describe your city. Create a pie chart or bar graph to present the information you have chosen.

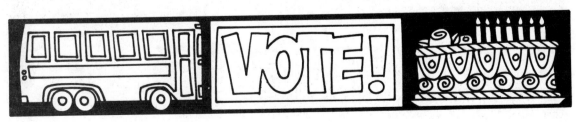

Create a City
© The Learning Works, Inc.

Name _____

Group Worksheet I

Have one person from your group fill in the final decisions your group made about your city. Give this worksheet to your teacher when it is complete.

Names of group members:

_____   _____

_____   _____

_____   _____

Name of our city: _____

The location of our city is as follows:

Latitude: _____

Longitude: _____

State: _____

Surrounding states: _____

Here is a short history of our city:

_____

_____

_____

_____

_____

_____

_____

_____

Name _____

Group Worksheet II

Have one person from your group write answers to the following questions about the physical features of your city. Turn in the completed worksheet to your teacher.

Name of our city: _____

The outstanding physical features of our city are:

_____

_____

_____

_____

Here are some of the positive effects these physical features have had on our city.

_____

_____

_____

_____

_____

Here are some of the negative effects these physical features have had on our city.

_____

_____

_____

_____

_____

Create a City
© The Learning Works, Inc.

Name _____

Group Worksheet III

Have one person from your group record the final decisions your group made about the cultural diversity and demographics of your city. Hand in this worksheet when it is complete.

Describe the variety of ethnic cultures that exists in your city. Describe one of the special celebrations and traditions that typifies each ethnic culture.

_____

_____

_____

_____

_____

_____

_____

_____

Write a short paragraph describing the demographics of the city you are creating.

_____

_____

_____

_____

_____

_____

_____

_____

_____

_____

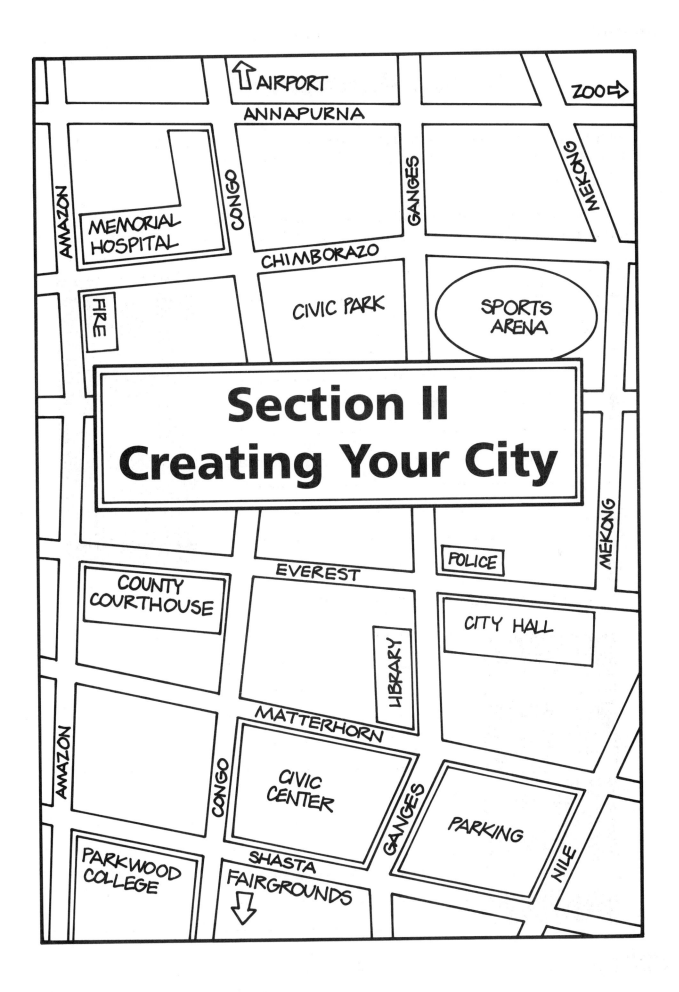

Section II
Creating Your City

Name _____

Government

Most large American cities are organized under charters and have a mayor and a city council. A charter is a document similar to a constitution in that it gives certain rights and freedoms to the citizens and outlines rules for governing. In this form of government, the city council makes the laws and approves the city budget. The mayor is the executive and is responsible for the overall administration of the city government. There are often variations in the structure of the government. In some cities, the mayors serve on the city council, while in others, they remain separate. Boston has a mayor-council system, with the mayor serving four years and the council members serving two years. New York City has a mayor who is elected for four years and is in charge of the management of the entire city. There are also five borough presidents who advise the mayor on issues relating to their boroughs.

Local City Information

Complete this form with information about the government of the city or town where you live.

Name and title of current leader _____

Length of term of office _____

What responsibilities does the leader have? _____

_____

_____

Who assists the leader in organizing and running the government? _____

_____

_____

How are these people selected? _____

_____

What are the primary duties of these individuals? _____

_____

Does your city have a charter? _____

If so, on what date was the charter adopted? _____

If not, what other document defines the powers of the city government? _____

_____

Name _____

Government
(continued)

With your group, decide on the form of government your city will have. Record your answers to the following questions on a separate piece of paper:

1. Who is the current leader of your city government and what is this person's title?
   - How is the leader selected for the job, and what is the term of office?
   - Describe the qualifications a person must have to hold this office.

2. What is the legislative, or lawmaking, body of your city called?
   - How many members are part of this body?
   - How are legislative members selected, and what are their terms of office?
   - What are the powers and duties of the legislative body?

3. Name any other special boards or commissions that help to run your government. How do they work?

Create a city charter in the space below. Include a list of the citizens' rights, and outline some of the powers of the city's governing officials.

_____ **City Charter**

_____

_____

_____

_____

_____

_____

_____

_____

_____

_____

_____

_____

Create a City
© The Learning Works, Inc.

Name _____

Business and Industry

Every city or town has businesses and industries that help support the community. New York City's leading businesses and industries include publishing, textiles and fashion, tourism, commercial shipping, and finance. Some cities have a major business or industry with which they are identified. For example, Detroit, Michigan, is identified with automobile manufacturing; Hartford, Connecticut, is called the insurance capital of the United States; and Los Angeles, California, is associated with the entertainment industry. A city may be identified with one particular corporation. For example, Kansas City, Missouri, is associated with Hallmark Cards Inc., and Rochester, New York, is associated with the Eastman Kodak Company. In a small to moderate-sized town, this company may be the major employer of the town's work force.

List some of the major businesses and industries located in the city in which you live. Describe the products and/or services provided by each.

1. _____

   _____

2. _____

   _____

3. _____

   _____

4. _____

   _____

5. _____

   _____

PENNSYLVANIA

Hershey

Name _____

Business and Industry
(continued)

Brainstorm with your group and decide on two businesses or industries that will be major employers in your new city. Complete the following information for each.

Business/industry name _____

Describe the product(s) and/or service(s) provided by the company _____

_____

_____

Business/industry name _____

Describe the product(s) and/or service(s) provided by the company _____

_____

_____

What will you do to attract these businesses to your city? _____

_____

_____

_____

_____

On a separate piece of paper, design a company logo and write a motto for each of the companies listed above.

Name _____

Education

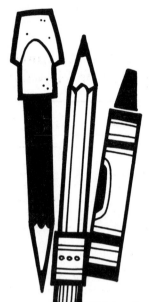

Formal education is an important part of city life. By acquiring an education, students develop the skills and knowledge they need to become useful members of society. Most large cities have public and private schools, colleges, and universities. New York City has the largest public school system in the nation with approximately 960 schools. Many of its high schools are specialized and offer particular training in areas such as the performing arts, science, and aviation. Schools across the country provide special help for students with learning disabilities and for non-English-speaking students. In most cities, property taxes and state aid help to pay the cost of educating students in a constantly changing society.

Fill in the report card below for the school that you now attend.

School Report Card

Is the school public or private? _____

Grade levels: _____

Student/teacher ratio: _____

Total hours of instructional time per day: _____

Total enrollment: _____

Special academic programs (for example, gifted and talented):_____

_____

Special school facilities (for example, computer room): _____

_____

Extracurricular programs (for example, sports activities or music classes):_____

_____

The grade I give my school is: _____

The reason for that grade is: _____

_____

Name _____

Education
(continued)

With the other members of your group, discuss the educational system you would like to develop for your new city. Have one person in your group fill in the following information:

Number of public schools: _____

Number of private schools: _____

Types of specialized schools (example: vocational): _____

Name the colleges and/or universities located in your city. _____

_____

How many hours do students spend per day in a formal instructional situation?

_____

What is the average student-teacher ratio in your school system? _____

_____

How are the students evaluated? _____

_____

How are the schools evaluated? _____

_____

Who is in charge of your school system? What are this person's responsibilities?

_____

_____

What special or innovative curriculum is provided for the students? _____

_____

_____

How is education funded in your city? _____

_____

Name _____

Architecture

Many cities are identified with a particular style of architecture. The seaside resort of Cape May, New Jersey, is nationally known for its Victorian homes. New Orleans, Louisiana, is famous for its French Quarter, where you will find many examples of French Colonial buildings with their intricate iron balconies and grillwork. When a town is known for a particular style, the town leaders sometimes make it a law that all new buildings be constructed in that same style.

Victorian
This style of architecture is recognized by its highly ornate look. Decorative pieces of trim are added to the windows and roof lines. These are usually painted in contrasting colors. Victorian homes usually have large covered porches.

Georgian Colonial
A form of classical architecture, this style became popular during the 17th and 18th centuries. Georgian Colonial is a revival of the styles of ancient Greeks and Romans. You can recognize this style by its use of columns and simple, symmetrical lines.

Cape Cod
This style of architecture, first developed on Cape Cod, Massachusetts, in the 18th and early 19th centuries, is usually reserved for houses and is recognized by its dormer windows. Early Cape Cod cottages were simple, one-story wooden houses with gabled roofs, massive central chimneys, and partial basements.

With your group, briefly research the following styles of architecture: colonial, classical, Spanish, and modern. If examples of a particular architectural style exist where you live, list them here:

_____

_____

Try to locate examples in your city of the following architectural elements: dormer, dome, column, fanlight, and pediment.

Name _____

Architecture
(continued)

Brainstorm with your group and create at least three structures for your new city. Record the information about the buildings in the spaces provided.

Architectural style of first building _____

What is the purpose of this building? _____

_____

Explain your choice of style. _____

_____

Architectural style of second building _____

What is the purpose of this building? _____

_____

Explain your choice of style. _____

_____

Architectural style of a typical home in your new city _____

_____

Explain your choice of style. _____

_____

On a separate piece of paper, draw a picture of one of the homes in your new city. If you prefer, you can build a model of a home to display at City Celebrations Day.

Name _____

Shopping and Dining

Walk down the Magnificent Mile in Chicago, Illinois; the famed Fifth Avenue in New York City; and the ritzy Rodeo Drive in Los Angeles, California, and you'll be on some of the best shopping streets in America. From secondhand clothing stores and quaint antique shops to stylish boutiques and large department stores, cities offer a wealth of shopping opportunities for all.

The cultural diversity of a city is often reflected in its restaurants. In larger cities, you can often dine on a variety of ethnic foods. Certain cities may be known for specialty restaurants. The Fisherman's Wharf area in San Francisco, California, is a great place to dine if you enjoy seafood. If you like Cajun food, you can't beat New Orleans, Louisiana.

A Shopping and Dining Guide

Pretend that you are taking a visitor out to shop and dine in your home city or town. Write short guidebook entries describing some of your town's best shopping and dining spots.

Shopping areas: _____

_____

_____

_____

_____

_____

_____

_____

Dining out: _____

_____

_____

_____

_____

_____

_____

_____

Name _____

Shopping and Dining
(continued)

With the other members of your group, brainstorm ideas to design some of the shopping and dining facilities located in the city you are creating.

Describe two of the stores that are located in your new city. Explain what kinds of merchandise these stores sell, and why these stores are attractive to customers.

Store #1: _____

_____

_____

_____

Store #2: _____

_____

_____

_____

Design two restaurants for your new city. For each restaurant, describe the type of food served, the ambiance or the appearance of the restaurant, the location, and the average price of a meal.

Restaurant #1: _____

_____

_____

_____

Restaurant #2: _____

_____

_____

_____

_____

On a separate piece of paper, create an ad for a store or restaurant in your new city.

Name _____

Transportation

Modes of transportation that move materials and people into and out of a city include highways, railways, waterways, and air travel. Not all kinds of transportation are available or necessary to all cities. The systems used depend upon the needs of the people and the geography of the area. For example, ferry service is important to the people of Seattle, Washington. Many residents of New York City depend on the subway system and taxi service. San Francisco is famous for its cable cars.

With the other members of your group, brainstorm a list of the most important transportation modes used in the city or town where you live.

_____

_____

_____

_____

_____

↑MONORAIL
SUBWAY↓

List the names of some of the more unusual transportation modes that members of your group have used. Briefly describe each one.

1. _____

_____

2. _____

_____

3. _____

_____

4. _____

_____

5. _____

_____

Name _____

Transportation
(continued)

Work with the members of your group to create transportation systems for your new city. Be original and creative. Put a new spin on an old idea. Record your answers in the spaces provided.

_____ **Department of Transportation**

Transportation within your city:

Type of system: _____

Description of how it operates: _____

_____

Reason for selection: _____

Type of system: _____

Description of how it operates: _____

_____

Reason for selection: _____

AIRPORT →

HARBOR ↑

Transportation from your city to other places:

Type of system: _____

Description of how it operates: _____

_____

Reason for selection: _____

Type of system: _____

Description of how it operates: _____

_____

Reason for selection: _____

Name _____

Landmarks

Most cities have landmarks that are significant in some way. A landmark may be a noteworthy structure, building, monument, or geographical feature that is important to the city area or to the entire nation. Philadelphia, Pennsylvania, a city rich in history, has many famous landmarks. Independence Hall, where the Second Continental Congress drafted the Declaration of Independence, and the Liberty Bell, our nation's symbol of freedom, are both located there. Camelback Mountain is a Phoenix, Arizona, landmark. The Empire State Building in New York City, and the Lincoln and Washington Memorials of Washington, D.C., are other examples of notable landmarks.

With your group, discuss landmarks located in your region of the country. List some of them and explain briefly why you consider them to be noteworthy.

1. _____

_____

_____

2. _____

_____

_____

3. _____

_____

_____

4. _____

_____

_____

5. _____

_____

_____

Landmarks
(continued)

Brainstorm with your group and decide on two landmarks that will be significant sites in your new city. Fill in the following information about them.

Name one major city landmark. _____

_____

Describe the landmark. Tell about its appearance. What materials were used in its construction? If it is a natural feature, explain why it is unusual.

_____

_____

_____

_____

Why is this landmark important to your city? _____

_____

_____

Name a second city landmark. _____

_____

Describe the landmark. Tell about its appearance. What materials were used in its construction? If it is a natural feature, explain why it is unusual.

_____

_____

_____

_____

Why is this landmark important to your city? _____

_____

_____

Using white construction paper, create a postcard featuring a picture of one of your city's landmarks.

Name _____

Climate

The term *climate* is used to describe the average weather a region experiences over a long period of time. Climate is different from weather. Weather is the precipitation, wind conditions, and temperature of a region over a short period of time. The daily weather conditions a region experiences over a period of years make up the climate of an area. Weather may change quickly and often. Climates may change, but the change is slow and gradual.

No matter where you live, climate affects your life in many ways. It determines the plant and animal life of an area, the style of architecture, the available local food, and your choices of clothing, transportation, and recreational activities. The most important factor in determining climate is latitude. Other influences include physical features and proximity to large bodies of water.

Some of the major climates recognized by meteorologists are tropical wet, highlands, desert, steppe, subtropic moist, oceanic moist, and subarctic. Maps showing the locations of these climates can be found in atlases and other reference books. Use these reference sources to complete the chart below.

City	Climate Type	Average Daily Temperature	Average Yearly Precipitation
Anchorage, AK			
Denver, CO			
Honolulu, HI			
Phoenix, AZ			
Miami, FL			

The climate where I live is _____

It is influenced by _____

Name _____

Climate
(continued)

With the members of your group, choose a climate for your new city. Your choice of climate should be consistent with your city's latitude and any nearby influences, such as oceans, lakes, mountains, and other physical features. Use the information your group develops to complete the chart below.

The climate of our new city is _____

Month	Average Daily Temperature	Average Monthly Precipitation
January		
February		
March		
April		
May		
June		
July		
August		
September		
October		
November		
December		

Create a City
© The Learning Works, Inc.

Name _____

Cultural Life

Our nation's cities are rich in cultural attractions such as theater, opera, and ballet performances, as well as a variety of museum exhibits. In Chicago, the Art Institute is well known for its excellent French Impressionist collection. The city's Museum of Science and Industry contains an underground coal mine. New York City has many types of museums. Its Metropolitan Museum of Art houses a large collection of art treasures from around the world. The area around Broadway is home to the famous theater district where you can see outstanding theatrical performances.

List the names of some of the cultural attractions that members of your group have visited. Write a sentence or two about what was observed in each place and why the experience was valuable.

1. _____
   _____
   _____

2. _____
   _____
   _____

3. _____
   _____
   _____

4. _____
   _____
   _____

5. _____
   _____
   _____

Name _____

Cultural Life
(continued)

Brainstorm with the other members of your group to create three cultural attractions for your new city. Record information about the three cultural attractions in the spaces below. For ideas, review the previous page, or research the cultural life of other cities.

Cultural Guide to _____

Name of first attraction: _____

Highlights of performance or exhibit: _____

_____

_____

Name of second attraction: _____

Highlights of performance or exhibit: _____

_____

_____

Name of third attraction: _____

Highlights of performance or exhibit: _____

_____

_____

Create a City
© The Learning Works, Inc.

Recreation

Parks, playgrounds, beaches, and sports facilities are just a few of the places people can enjoy recreational activities in large cities. New York City's Central Park is located in the heart of Manhattan. The park is home to a lake, playgrounds, wooded areas, jogging trails, athletic fields, and a concert area. War Memorial Park, a popular recreational area in Little Rock, Arkansas, has a 33-acre zoo. Residents of Boston, Massachusetts, enjoy canoeing and sailing on the Charles River. The climate and location of Los Angeles, California, provide ample opportunities for its residents to participate in golfing, surfing, and swimming throughout the year.

Recreational Facilities
in the City or Town Where You Live

Fill in this Recreation Department form for the city or town where you live.

Names and sizes of park areas: _____

_____

_____

_____

Types of sports facilities: _____

_____

_____

Special recreational events: _____

_____

_____

_____

Zoos (if applicable): _____

_____

Names of beaches (if applicable): _____

_____

Types of playgrounds: _____

_____

_____

Name _____

Recreation
(continued)

With your group, design a public recreation area for the city you are creating. Use the guidelines on this page to help you develop your facility. Then draw a sketch of the recreation area at the bottom of this page. Your group may wish to create a model of the recreation area for City Celebrations Day.

Type of recreation area: _____

Size and location of recreation area: _____
_____

Types of playground equipment: _____
_____

Types of sports facilities: _____
_____

Garden, lake, or pond areas: _____
_____
_____

Special events held here: _____
_____

Sketch of Recreation Area in the City of
_____

Create a City
© The Learning Works, Inc.

Creating a Budget

A budget is a plan for raising and spending money. The idea is to plan so that money spent does not exceed the amount of money raised. Every city and town needs to create a budget to guide its spending each year and operate effectively. In most cases, cities and towns get money, or *revenue*, by collecting taxes from its residents and businesses. State and federal governments also send money to cities to provide certain services. The money collected pays for things such as trash collection, snow removal, street repairs, installation of street lights, recreation programs, and police and fire protection. The city or town also uses the revenue it receives to build and maintain public buildings, such as schools, libraries, and city government offices.

- With your group, brainstorm a list of other things that the city government is responsible for providing.

- Compare your group's list with the lists compiled by the other groups. Perhaps there are items that you've forgotten. Add any new items to your list.

- If possible, invite a representative from your city government to visit your class to discuss the city's budget. Prepare a list of questions to ask your visitor.

The pie charts below represent the city budget of "Somewhere, U.S.A."

Sources of Revenue   Expenses

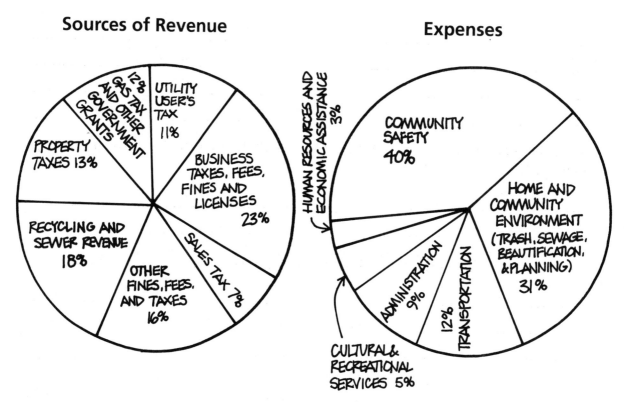

Name _____

Creating a Budget
(continued)

Usually the preparation of a city budget follows this procedure:

1. Each department (such as recreation, public works, police, and fire) submits a departmental budget outlining their needs—for example, payroll and equipment—and the associated costs of each.

2. The city council, town committee, or mayor's budget department reviews these lists and makes suggestions. (Each department may be required to rewrite its list several times.)

3. A final budget is prepared. In some cities, a public hearing or election may be held to approve the budget.

Do research to find the yearly cost of providing these services where you live:

- fire protection
- police protection
- public library

With your group, prepare a budget for your new city. Imagine that you are starting with 10 million dollars in revenue. Refer to the list of services your group made previously. Decide what services your city will provide and how much money will be spent on each. List the items and amounts here.

_____   _____
_____   _____
_____   _____
_____   _____
_____   _____

Were there any things you were not able to include because there was not enough money? If so, list them here.

_____   _____
_____   _____

Explain how your group decided what your city could and could not afford.

_____
_____
_____

Name _____

City Council Debates

Many cities are governed by an elected group called the "city council." The people of a city vote to elect these representatives to do the business of the city. The number of council members and the term of office varies from city to city. In some cities, the council members elect a mayor or council president from among themselves. In other cities, the citizens elect the mayor.

The council meets regularly to discuss and decide the rules of the city and what services the city will provide. The council must decide, for example, if and when to build a new library, whether to add officers to the police force, how to attract businesses, whether the city should have a recycling program, and what the penalties should be for the owners of barking dogs.

What are some of the issues facing your community that have recently been debated? (for example: graffiti, property maintenance, teen curfews, etc.) If you need help, check the local newspaper, call your city hall, or check with a city council or township committee member. List three of the issues here:

1. _____

2. _____

3. _____

Choose one of the issues and list the pros and cons of one of the proposed solutions in the columns provided.

Pros	Cons
_____	_____
_____	_____
_____	_____
_____	_____
_____	_____
_____	_____

Name _____

City Council Debates
(continued)

Within your group, discuss the idea of skateboarding on the public sidewalks of your new city. Should it be permitted? Try to see the issue from the point of view of store owners, the public, and the skateboarders. Brainstorm a list of reasons why it should be allowed, and write them below in the "Pros" column. Then think of a list of reasons why it should not be allowed, and write these in the "Cons" column.

Pros	Cons

Name _____

City Statistics

Work with the other members of your group to complete this "City Statistics" form for the city you are creating.

Population of your city: _____

Founded by: _____

Founding date: _____

Land area: _____

Land elevation: _____

Employment rate (use percentages): _____

Average home price: _____

Average income per household: _____

City tax rate (use percentages): _____

Names of city neighborhood areas (examples: downtown, West side, East side, etc.):

_____

_____

_____

City services (examples: fire protection, trash collection, water)

_____

_____

_____

_____

_____

Name _____

Reporting About Your City

Pretend that you and the other members of your group have been elected to serve as city council members. Your first task is to compile a "City Council Study" to provide more details about the many features of your city. Each person in your group will write one or more sections of this report.

Once all of the sections have been written, edited, and revised, your group members should put them together in one comprehensive report.

Follow these steps:

1. In your group, decide who will write about each of the topics listed below.

2. Write that person's name next to the topic, along with the date the work is due.

	Name	Date due
Government	_____	_____
Business and Industry	_____	_____
Education	_____	_____
Architecture	_____	_____
Shopping and Dining	_____	_____
Transportation	_____	_____
Landmarks	_____	_____
Climate	_____	_____
Cultural Life	_____	_____
Recreation	_____	_____
City Statistics	_____	_____
City Budget	_____	_____
City Council Debates	_____	_____

Name _____

Reporting About Your City
(continued)

Each person in your group should do the following for each of his or her topics:

1. Write a one- to two-page report describing in detail that aspect of city life.

2. Edit, proofread, and revise the report to create a final draft.

You can put the sections of your City Council Study together in any order you choose. With your group, decide on the order you will use and record it below.

City Council Study
Contents

1. _____
2. _____
3. _____
4. _____
5. _____
6. _____
7. _____
8. _____
9. _____
10. _____
11. _____
12. _____
13. _____

COUGARS

CONESTOGA

AS FRIENDLY AS THE WEST, AS MODERN AS TOMORROW!

Section III
Project Ideas

Name _____

It's Travel Time

As a travel agent for the Fly Away Travel Company, it is your task to design a trip to your new city. Fill in the Travel Information Form for your clients to advise them of what they need to know before they leave on vacation to visit your city.

Travel Information Form

Date of departure: _____

Climate: _____
_____

What to pack: _____
_____
_____

Hotels: _____
_____
_____

Restaurants: _____
_____
_____

Special events: _____
_____
_____
_____

Recreational facilities: _____
_____
_____

Emergency services: _____
_____
_____

Name _____

Create a Travel Poster

Your new city is an exciting place to visit, with a full assortment of interesting sights, fine restaurants, great shopping, excellent cultural attractions, varied recreational facilities, and unique special events. It's your job to design a travel poster that describes the highlights of your city in a creative and eye-catching way. Pictures of points of interest in your new city should appear on your travel poster.

Some cities include special slogans on their travel posters. For example, the Boston Tourist Bureau has used the phrase "Boston Overnight, Just for the Fun of It!" as its slogan on travel advertisements and posters.

Sketch your poster ideas in the spaces below. Then use posterboard to create a final version. Display your completed poster during City Celebrations Day.

Name _____

Regional Food Fest

Many areas of our country are known for their special styles of cooking or for particular foods. New England is known for its pot roasts and soups called chowders. Lobsters are closely identified with the coastal cities of Maine. Maryland is famous for its crab dishes. Philadelphia, Pennsylvania, is famous for sandwiches called "Philly cheesesteaks."

There are ethnic variations of the same food. For example, the American "pancake" is basically the same thing as the French "crepe," the Middle Eastern "pita bread," the Italian "calzone," the Jewish "blintz," and the Mexican "tortilla."

Brainstorm with your group and choose foods to represent your city. Use the space below to record your ideas.

The foods chosen to represent our city are:

1. _____

2. _____

3. _____

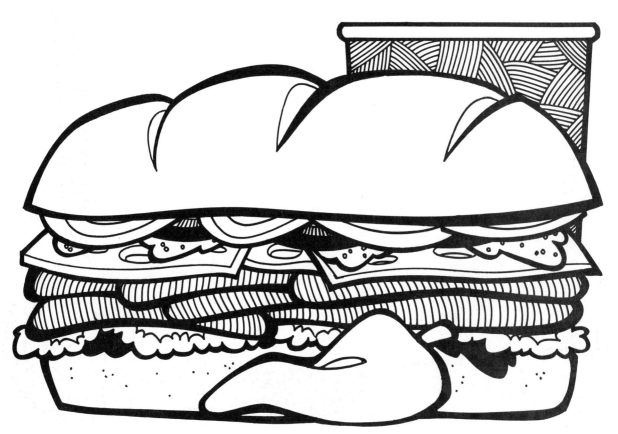

Name _____

Regional Food Fest
(continued)

Now that your group has chosen some of the foods that represent your city, use the space below to write a recipe for a regional dish. The recipe should include the ingredients, instructions, and any special equipment needed for its preparation.

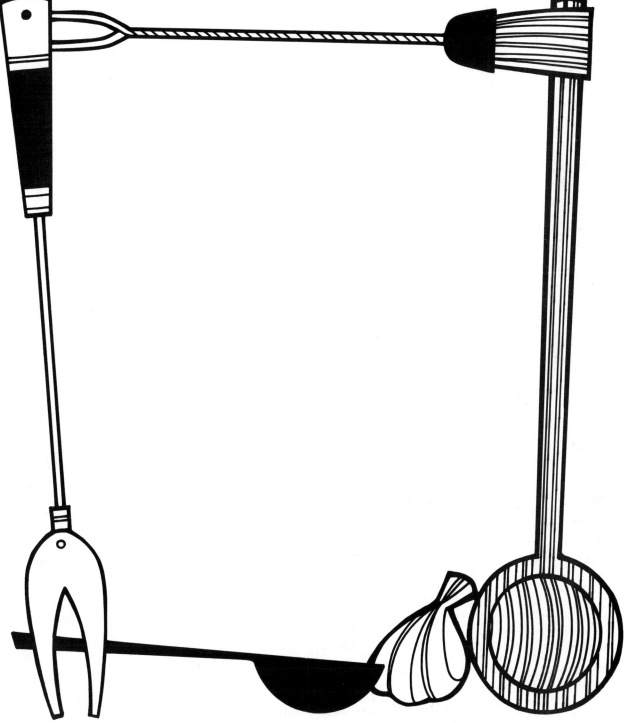

Name _____

City Symbols

Most American cities have flags and seals. The words and pictures on the flag or seal usually tell something about the city. For example, the stars on Chicago's flag stand for Fort Dearborn, the Great Chicago Fire, and the two Chicago-based world's fairs. The city seal of Phoenix contains a picture of a phoenix, the mythical bird for which the city is named.

With the other members of your group, design a flag and a seal for your new city. Use scratch paper to work out your ideas. When your group has decided on the final designs, create your city flag and seal using construction paper. Use the lines below to explain the meaning of the words and pictures that appear on the flag and seal. Display your city flag and seal on City Celebrations Day.

Explanation of words and pictures on city flag:

_____
_____
_____
_____
_____
_____
_____
_____

Explanation of words and pictures on city seal:

_____
_____
_____
_____
_____
_____
_____
_____

Map Your City

As a group, create a map that will show the following city locations:

- municipal areas
- major business and industry sites
- residential neighborhoods
- schools, libraries, and museums
- historic attractions
- park areas
- entertainment centers

On your map, include the names of main streets and important physical features. Provide a *key* at the bottom of the map with clearly distinguishable symbols. A sample map key is shown below. Use the bottom of this page to sketch your map ideas. Include your completed map as part of your exhibit during City Celebrations Day.

Name _____

Musical Tribute

City names are often featured in popular songs. For example, many songs have been written about New York City. "The Sidewalks of New York" and "New York, New York" are two favorites. "My Kind of Town" musically describes Chicago, and "I Left My Heart In San Francisco" describes that great city in song.

Create an official song for your new city. Make up original lyrics and set them to a familiar tune, or create your own music. You will perform your song for visitors on City Celebrations Day.

Use the lines below to write your ideas.

_____

_____

_____

_____

_____

_____

_____

_____

_____

_____

_____

_____

_____

_____

_____

Name _____

Create a Professional Sports Team

Professional sports teams exist in many cities. There are professional leagues for such sports as baseball, basketball, football, ice hockey, and soccer. Create a professional sports team for your city. Your group may choose one of the sports listed above or select another sport. Your group may even want to create an original sport.

The game or sport we chose to represent our city is _____ .

- Name your team. The name of your team should have some connection to your city. Your team name might reflect something about your city's past or future, your city's location, or a product for which your city is well known.

- Design a uniform for your team. Consider colors and a logo that can be used on jackets, hats, shirts, pants, etc. On a separate sheet of paper, draw and color a picture of a team member in uniform.

- If you are creating a new game, write a rule book describing how the game is played. You may wish to include illustrations and/or diagrams.

- As a group project, build a model of your team's stadium or playing field to be shared at City Celebrations Day.

- Will your team have a mascot? If so, draw a picture of your mascot on a separate sheet of white art paper, or dress up a doll or stuffed animal as your mascot.

- Design a pennant or banner for your new sports team.

Create a City
© The Learning Works, Inc.

City Mural

Think of your newly created city as an environment—a habitat for the many people living there. With members of your group, sketch, draw, or paint a mural showing various features of your city. You may want to include the buildings, transportation systems, and physical features that you previously created. Share your city with others by displaying your mural at City Celebrations Day.

Work with the other members of your group to decide who will be responsible for each part of the mural and what materials will be needed.

Use the space below to sketch your ideas. Then meet with your group to plan and create the final version of the mural.

Name _____

City Poetry

Throughout history, cities have inspired poets. Some poets create unusual comparisons in their compositions about cities. For example, in his poem "Trip: San Francisco," poet Langston Hughes compares the bridges that span the waterways to cobwebs in the sky.

Write a poem about the city in which you live. In your poem, describe something that you've observed that reminds you of something else. Think about the many sights and sounds of your city; try to include some of these details as well.

_____
Title of Your Poem

_____

_____

_____

_____

_____

_____

_____

_____

_____

_____

_____

_____

_____

Here are some city poems to read and enjoy:

"Winds of a Windy City" by Carl Sandburg
"Fog" by Carl Sandburg
"City Rain" by Rachel Field
"City Streets—Country Roads" by Eleanor Farjeon
"City" by Langston Hughes

Name _____

The Big Story

Imagine that you are a reporter for your city newspaper. Exciting things are happening in your city today. Describe them in a news story. Be sure to use who, what, where, when, and why questions to help you relate the details of your story. First, create a name for your newspaper, and write it in the large horizontal box. Add the paper's date on the blank line. Then write a headline for your story and, in the small box, include a "photo" taken at the scene.

¢

Annual Events

Every year on New Year's Day, colorfully dressed marchers called *mummers* parade up Philadelphia's Broad Street to the delight of thousands of onlookers. String bands play their special music as the city celebrates its annual parade. In New Orleans, people participate in the exciting festivities of the annual Mardi Gras celebration by traveling through the city streets on decorated floats and attending costume balls.

What special annual observance takes place in your city? With your group, brainstorm five original ideas, and write them in the space below.

1. _____
2. _____
3. _____
4. _____
5. _____

Working as a group, select your best idea and develop a newspaper advertisement to announce the event. Tell about the history of the event and when and where it will be held. Use the space below to sketch your ideas. Create your final ad on a separate piece of paper to display during City Celebrations Day.

61

Name _____

Wish You Were Here

Imagine that you are a tourist visiting your new city. Write a postcard home to a friend or family member telling about your experiences. On one side of the post-card, draw a picture of a favorite city attraction. On the other, write your message.

Name _____

Create a Character

In every city and town, there are certain people who are well known locally. Often, these individuals are known because of contributions they have made to benefit their communities.

Think about some of the prominent or well-known people in the town or city where you live. Do research to learn the names of men and women from your community who have made contributions in each of the areas listed below. List at least one person for each category. (You may list people from the present or the past.) For each person you list, briefly describe one of his or her accomplishments.

Government/public service _____

_____

Education _____

_____

Sports _____

_____

Fund-raising/charity work _____

_____

Medicine _____

_____

Fine arts or performing arts _____

_____

What qualities do these people have in common? _____

_____

_____

_____

Name _____

Create a Character
(continued)

Now that you have thought about well-known citizens in the city where you live, invent a famous citizen for the new city you've created. You'll want to create a "model citizen" who has made contributions in some way to the community. Working with the other members of your group, fill in the information on this page and page 65 to create a profile of this imaginary citizen.

Person's name: _____

Age: _____   Date of birth: _____

Why is this person famous? _____

_____

_____

_____

Education and/or training: _____

Occupation(s): _____

Volunteer groups or social groups to which this person belongs: _____

_____

_____

Describe any hardships this person may have had to overcome. _____

_____

_____

_____

_____

Name _____

Create a Character
(continued)

Describe this person's character or personality. _____

_____

_____

_____

_____

Describe this person's appearance. _____

_____

_____

_____

Is there something about this person's dress or appearance that is memorable? (For example: He is never seen without his hat and walking stick. She always wears something purple.)

_____

_____

_____

_____

What contributions has this person made to the community? _____

_____

_____

_____

_____

_____

Create a City
© The Learning Works, Inc.

Name _____

Create a Character
(continued)

Draw a "portrait" of your city's famous citizen on this page.

Name _____

Create a Character
(continued)

Use the information on pages 64–65 to write a biographical sketch of the famous citizen that your group has created. Write a rough draft using the lines below. Then create a final draft on a separate piece of paper. Include the portrait you created on page 66 as part of your completed project. Here are some things to keep in mind while you prepare your report:

- Describe the person's early, middle, and later life.

- Write in the third person.

- Focus on the citizen's contributions to the community.

Biographical Sketch of _____

_____

_____

_____

_____

_____

_____

_____

_____

_____

_____

_____

_____

_____

_____

Create a City
© The Learning Works, Inc.

Name _____

Meet the Character

Everyone present at City Celebrations Day will have the opportunity to meet the famous citizen your group created in the "Create a Character" activity (pages 63–67). Create a costume for this citizen based on the biographical information you prepared. What props will he or she need? Which group member will be responsible for supplying which things? Decide who in the group will portray the citizen. Record the information in the spaces provided.

Prop	Supplied by
1. _____	_____
2. _____	_____
3. _____	_____
4. _____	_____

_____ will be played by _____ .
citizen student

As a group, prepare a two-minute presentation that your citizen will give explaining the city as he or she knows it. Use the lines below to create an outline for your presentation.

_____
_____
_____
_____
_____
_____
_____
_____
_____
_____
_____
_____

Name _____

In Honor Of

Cities often publicly recognize the contributions of its citizens. This recognition may take several forms. Sometimes, a bridge, highway, or park is named for the person. In other cases, an existing location, such as a street or an airport, may be renamed. Another way to recognize an outstanding citizen is to build a statue, fountain, or other monument in his or her honor.

What parts of your home town are named in honor of past or present citizens? Record the group's answers on the lines below. In addition to the examples listed above, think about schools, libraries, streets, stadiums, auditoriums, and museums.

Person honored	Item named for him or her
1. _____	_____
2. _____	_____
3. _____	_____

Now think of some ways that the city you are creating might honor outstanding citizens from the past or present. Record your ideas here. Select the group's favorite idea, then create a model or drawing of it to display during City Celebrations Day.

1. _____

2. _____

3. _____

Create a City
© The Learning Works, Inc.

City Scrapbook

Scrapbooks are used to preserve photographs, awards, and other mementos. Work with the other members of your group to create a city scrapbook filled with items that recall memorable events, people, and places in your city. For example, a ticket to a special city event might be an interesting keepsake.

Follow these steps to help you get started:

1. Determine what scrapbook items to include, and decide which group member will create each item.

2. Using the chart below, write each group member's name next to the memento he or she is creating and the date that the work is due.

3. Have each member of your group fill in the information requested below.

Student's name	Scrapbook memento	Date due

Name _____

City Scrapbook
(continued)

Use this page to sketch a picture of and write information about the item you are creating for your group's city scrapbook. (This page should be duplicated so that each group member has a copy.)

My city's name: _____

My scrapbook memento: _____

Draw a sketch of your memento in the space below.

Materials I will need to construct my memento: _____

_____

_____

_____

My memento is important because: _____

_____

_____

When your group has finished creating the mementos, paste or attach them to the pages of the scrapbook. Be sure to include a label next to each item explaining the item's significance. Display the city scrapbook at your booth during City Celebrations Day.

Name _____

City Tour

Imagine that you are a tour guide for your new city. Which sites would you point out to visitors? Make a list of the five most fascinating places to see.

1. _____
2. _____
3. _____
4. _____
5. _____

Write a short informative talk about each of the above sites. Put yourself in the place of a visitor. What facts would be the most important and interesting to learn? Record your ideas on the lines below. Use scratch paper if you need more room.

_____
_____
_____
_____
_____
_____
_____
_____
_____
_____
_____
_____

Rehearse your talk. On City Celebrations Day, many "tourists" will come to see your city displays. You can take the visitors on a guided tour of your city by pointing out the models and displays in your exhibit, and by explaining the special features of the city in your informative talks.

Name _____

A Sense-ational City

People use all five senses—sight, smell, hearing, taste, and touch—as they collect and record memories. What places and experiences do you recall as you read the list below?

- warm sand underfoot
- bright neon lights
- fresh strawberry pie
- skyscrapers reflecting a sunset
- foghorns and rising mist
- band concerts in the park
- flags snapping in the wind
- cool polished marble

- shady lanes in quiet neighborhoods
- loud cheers at a sports arena
- spicy chili or steamy gumbo
- seagulls circling overhead
- sunny flower gardens
- the smoky smell of a barbecue
- the sound of a train's whistle
- splashing fountains

Many cities are famous for their sights, sounds, and smells. What would tourists remember after visiting the city you have created? Write at least one thing on each line below. Then create a poster picturing the things you have listed. Display your poster on City Celebrations Day.

sight: _____

smell: _____

hearing: _____

taste: _____

touch: _____

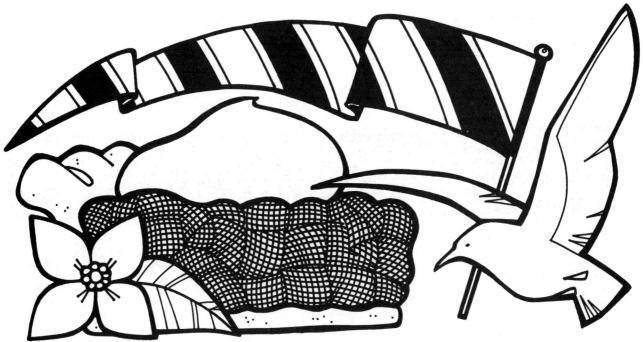

73

Name _____

Musical Performance

Each group will take turns performing the city songs they wrote for the "Musical Tribute" activity (page 56) for classmates, teachers, parents, and other visitors on City Celebrations Day.

Song title: _____

Length of time it will take to perform our song: _____

Names of students in our group who will perform the song:

_____

_____

_____

_____

_____

Type of musical accompaniment (example: piano, audio tape, etc.)

_____

For the presentation of your song, you could:

- mount the lyrics on a poster so that the audience can sing along

- make copies of the lyrics and distribute them during City Celebrations Day

- tape your song first, then sing along with the tape

- design props or costumes to enhance your presentation

- create dance steps to accompany the music

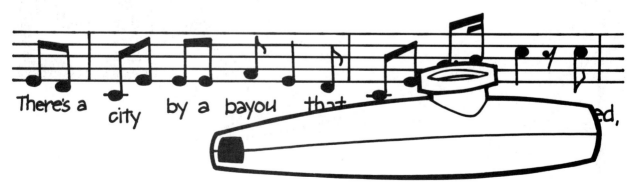

Name _____

City Shirts

Design a t-shirt that might be bought and worn by people visiting your city. It could feature your city's flag and/or seal, a catchy slogan, or pictures of landmarks. It might promote the local sports team or an annual event held in your city.

Sketch several ideas, then develop your favorite design into full-scale art done on poster board. You might even decorate actual shirts to wear on City Celebrations Day. Recycle old shirts by turning them inside-out, then adding your design with fabric paint or permanent markers.

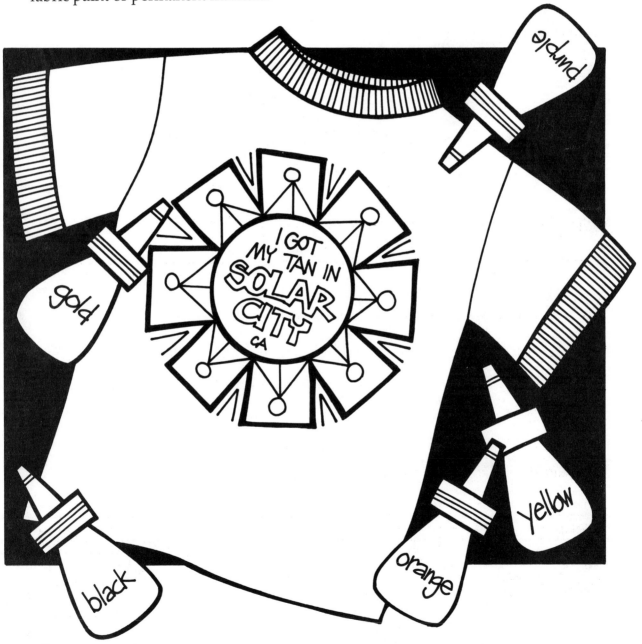

Create a City
© The Learning Works, Inc.

Name _____

Refreshment Stand

On City Celebrations Day, you may wish to offer refreshments to your guests. Working with the other members of your group, create a refreshment stand for your display area. At your stand, display a food that is popular in the region where your city is located. Work with the other members of your group to decide what food you would like to serve. (One of the student groups may wish to bring in a beverage, such as fruit punch, but be sure to get permission from your teacher first.)

After you have decided what food to serve, discuss the following questions with the members of your group:

• Who will prepare the food?

• How many portions will you need to prepare?

• Will you have copies of the recipe available for visitors to your booth?

• How will you decorate your refreshment stand to make it attractive? List your ideas below. You may want to make a sketch of your refreshment area on a piece of scratch paper.

_____

_____

_____

_____

_____

_____

• What supplies will you need—paper plates, serving utensils, toothpicks, napkins? Determine who will bring each item.

Student's name	Item they are bringing
_____	_____
_____	_____
_____	_____
_____	_____
_____	_____

ALOHA BAY COOLER

SAGUARO CITY SALSA HOT!

Section IV
City Celebrations Day

Pecan Creek Brownies

HARVEST HILL CHEESY POPCORN

City Celebrations Day
Planning Sheet I

Use the forms and planning sheets in this section to help you
in your preparations for City Celebrations Day.

Name of our city: _____

Date of City Celebrations Day: _____

Time: _____   Place: _____

Names of Group Members:

_____   _____

_____   _____

_____   _____

_____   _____

_____   _____

Projects to be displayed at our city booth: _____

_____

_____

_____

_____

_____

_____

Presentations our group will make: _____

_____

_____

_____

_____

_____

_____

Name _____

City Celebrations Day
Planning Sheet II

When your city booths are in place and ready to be viewed, you'll want to invite others to see them at City Celebrations Day. As a class, discuss who you would like to invite from your school.

List the staff members and classes to be invited.

_____   _____

_____   _____

_____   _____

_____   _____

_____   _____

_____   _____

Discuss who you would like to invite from your families. List the names of family members to be invited.

_____   _____

_____   _____

_____   _____

_____   _____

_____   _____

Decide who you would like to invite from your community. List the names of community members to be invited.

_____   _____

_____   _____

_____   _____

On page 81, you will find an invitation form. You can copy this sample invitation, or create one of your own. Use the completed invitations to invite people to City Celebrations Day. Divide up the guest lists you compiled above so that group members can share in writing the invitations. Each student will write a personal invitation to his or her own family members.

Create a City
© The Learning Works, Inc.

Name _____

Display Plan

Work with the other members of your group to determine how you will arrange the items in your display area on City Celebrations Day. Gather your materials and practice setting them up on your group's table. (The worksheet you completed on page 78 can be used as a checklist for your display items.) You may need to rearrange the items several times until your display area "works." Make sure everything is clearly marked so that visitors will have no trouble identifying your projects. After you agree upon an arrangement, have one member from your group sketch the arrangement in the space below. Use this sketch to guide you during setup on City Celebrations Day.

Invitation Form

Design an invitation to tell your parents, relatives, friends, classmates, classroom aides, administrators, and other teachers about City Celebrations Day. Here is a sample invitation to help you get started.

Dear _____ ,

We have been learning about cities in the United States and would like

to invite you to a special presentation entitled "City Celebrations Day"

to share what we have learned.

City Celebrations Day will be held on _____
(day/date)

in _____ . Our program will start at
(location)

_____ and continue until _____ .
(time)   (time)

Working in learning groups, we have created our own cities. Exhibits

at City Celebrations Day will include maps, models, posters, murals,

and musical performances. We will also be serving refreshments. We

hope that you will enjoy what we have created.

Sincerely,

_____

and class

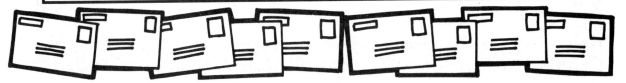

Thank-You Letter

The following letter could be used to thank participants as well as those parents, teachers, administrators, custodians, media specialists, or others who may have contributed to the success of your City Celebrations Day.

Dear _____,

Thank you for helping our class with City Celebrations Day. It was a

huge success! We really appreciated your assistance. If you had a chance

to visit, we hope that you enjoyed the exhibits and presentations.

Sincerely,

_____

and class

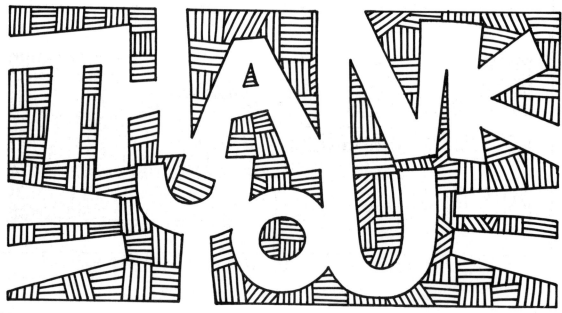

Certificate of Participation

City Celebrations Day

This certificate is issued to

_____

*in recognition of his or her participation
in a unit of study, "Create a City."*

_____   _____
           date   *signature of teacher*

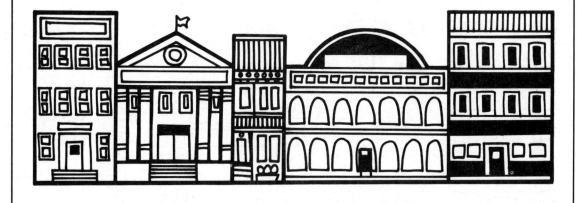

Create a City
© The Learning Works, Inc.

Name _____

Evaluation Form

Now that you have had a chance to learn about real cities and create an original one, please answer the following questions and return this form to your teacher.

1. List three new facts or concepts that you learned from this unit.

    A. _____

    B. _____

    C. _____

2. Which was your favorite activity? _____

    _____

    Why? _____

    _____

    _____

3. How well did your group work as a team? _____

    _____

    _____

5. What did you learn about yourself? _____

    _____

    _____